Pops 4

THIS PUBLICATION IS NOT AUTHORISED
FOR SALE IN THE UNITED STATES
OF AMERICA AND/OR CANADA.

Wise Publications
London/New York/Paris/Sydney/
Copenhagen/Madrid

Exclusive Distributors:
Music Sales Limited
8/9 Frith Street, London W1V 5TZ, England.
Music Sales Pty Limited
120 Rothschild Avenue, Rosebery, NSW 2018, Australia.

Order No. AM957858
ISBN 0-7119-7899-9
This book © Copyright 1999 by Wise Publications

Unauthorised reproduction of any part of this publication by any means
including photocopying is an infringement of copyright.

Compiled by Peter Evans
Music arranged by Stephen Duro
Music processed by Allegro Reproductions
Cover photograph (Geri Halliwell) courtesy of EMI Records

Printed in the United Kingdom by
Halstan & Co Limited, Amersham, Buckinghamshire.

Your Guarantee of Quality
As publishers, we strive to produce every book to the highest commercial standards.
The music has been freshly engraved and the book has been carefully designed to minimise
awkward page turns and to make playing from it a real pleasure.
Particular care has been given to specifying acid-free, neutral-sized paper made from pulps which have not been elemental
chlorine bleached. This pulp is from farmed sustainable forests and was produced with special regard for the environment.
Throughout, the printing and binding have been planned to ensure a sturdy, attractive publication which should give
years of enjoyment.
If your copy fails to meet our high standards, please inform us and we will gladly replace it.

Music Sales' complete catalogue describes thousands of titles and is available in full colour sections by subject,
direct from Music Sales Limited. Please state your areas of interest and send a cheque/postal order for £1.50 for postage to:
Music Sales Limited, Newmarket Road, Bury St. Edmunds, Suffolk IP33 3YB.

www.musicsales.co.uk

All I Have To Give *Backstreet Boys* 4

I'm Your Angel *Celine Dion/R. Kelly* 8

Look At Me *Geri Halliwell* 20

On A Day Like Today *Bryan Adams* 12

Perfect Moment *Martine McCutcheon* 16

She *Elvis Costello* 25

Sometimes *Britney Spears* 28

That Don't Impress Me Much *Shania Twain* 44

What Can I Do *The Corrs* 32

When The Going Gets Tough *Boyzone* 36

You Gotta Be *Des'ree* 40

All I Have To Give

Words & Music by Full Force

Moderately

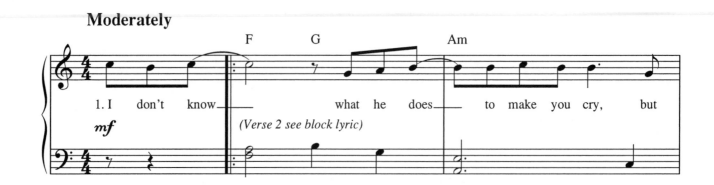

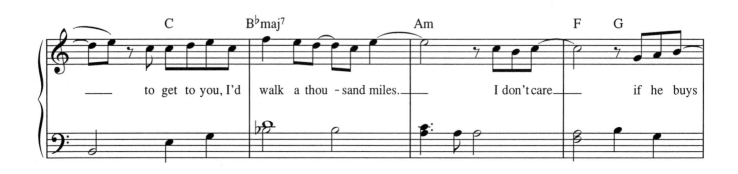

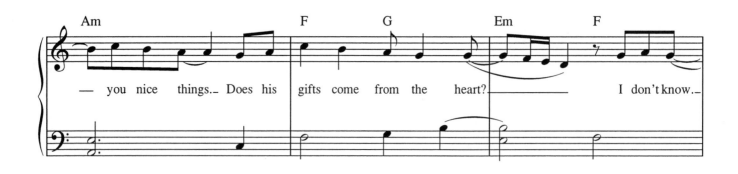

© Copyright 1997 P-Blast Music Incorporated & Zomba Enterprises Incorporated, USA.
Administered by Zomba Music Publishers Limited, 165-167 High Road, London NW10.
All Rights Reserved. International Copyright Secured.

But if you were my_____ girl,_____ I'd make it so we'd ne - ver be - a - part_____

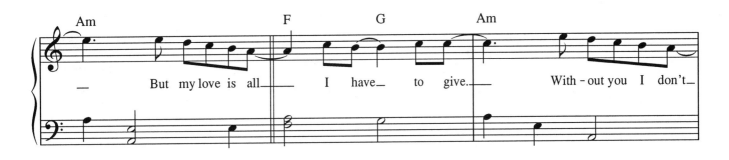

_____ But my love is all_____ I have__ to give._____ With - out you I don't__

_____ think I____ could live._____ I wish I could give_____ the world to you_____ but love is all I

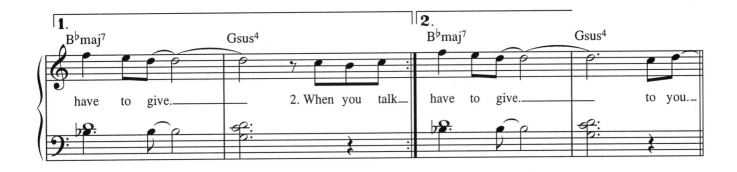

1. have____ to give._____ 2. When you talk__ **2.** have to give._____ to you._

_____ Hey girl,_____ I don't want you to cry no more____ in - side__

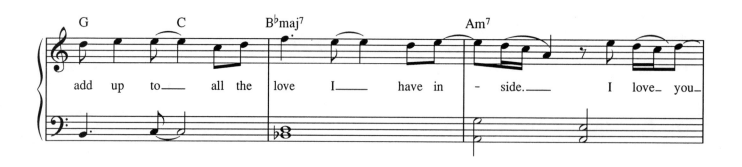

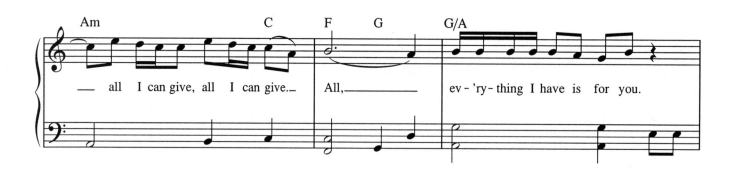

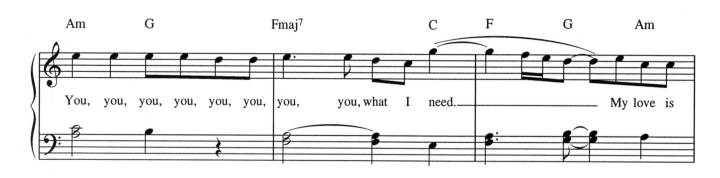

Verse 2:

When you talk does it seem like he's not
Even listening to a word you say?
That's okay babe, just tell me your problems
I'll try my best to kiss them all away.
Does he leave when you need hin the most?
Does his friends get all your time?
Baby please - I'm on my knees
Praying for the day that you'll be mine.

But my love is all I have to give *etc.*

I'm Your Angel

Words & Music by R. Kelly

Moderately slow

mf 1. No moun-tain's too high___ for you to climb.___ All___ you
(Verse 2 see block lyric)

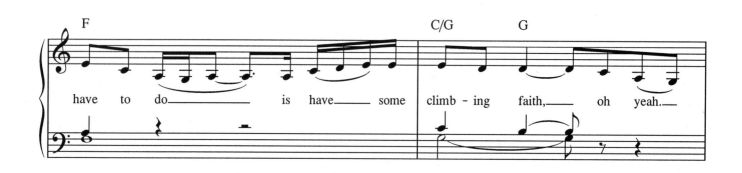

have to do___ is have___ some climb - ing faith,___ oh yeah.___

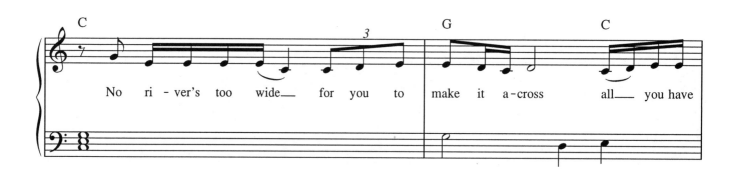

No ri - ver's too wide___ for you to make it a-cross all___ you have

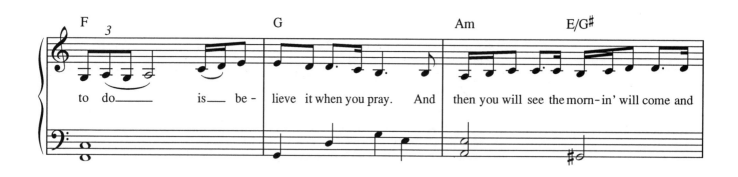

to do___ is___ be - lieve it when you pray. And then you will see the morn-in' will come and

© Copyright 1998 R. Kelly Publishing Incorporated & Zomba Songs Incorporated, USA.
Zomba Music Publishers Limited, 165-167 High Road, London NW10.
All Rights Reserved. International Copyright Secured.

ev - e - ry day will be bright_ as the sun.____ All of your fears,____ cast them on me,____

I just want you to see I'll be____ your____ cloud____ up in____ the sky,____ I'll be____ your

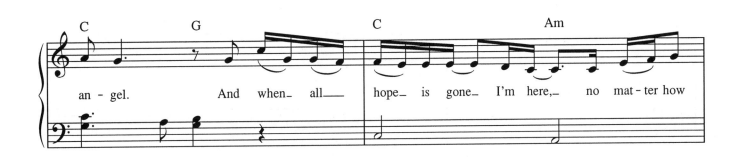

shoul - der when_ you cry.____ I hear your voi - ces when you call____ me, I am your

an - gel. And when_ all____ hope_ is gone_ I'm here,____ no mat - ter how

far____ you are____ I'm near.__ It makes no dif - fer - ence who you are,____ I am your

an - gel.___ I'm your an - gel.___

___ And when it's time to face the storm. I'll be___ right by your side. Grace will keep us safe and

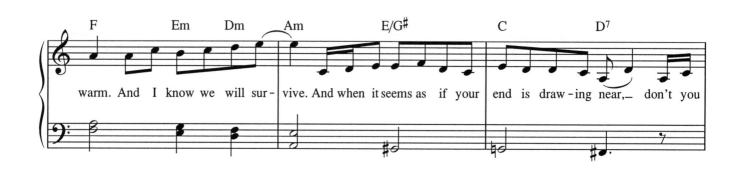

warm. And I know we will sur - vive. And when it seems as if your end is draw - ing near,___ don't you

ev - er give up___ the fight.___ Put your trust be - yond the stars.___ I'll be your

cloud___ up in___ the sky,___ I'll be___ your shoul - der when___ you cry.___ I hear your

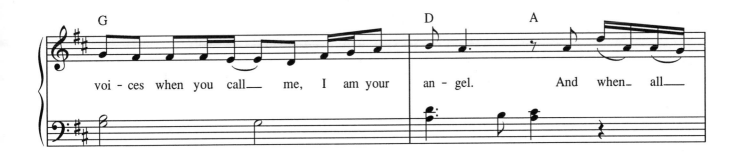

voi - ces when you call___ me, I am your an - gel. And when__ all__

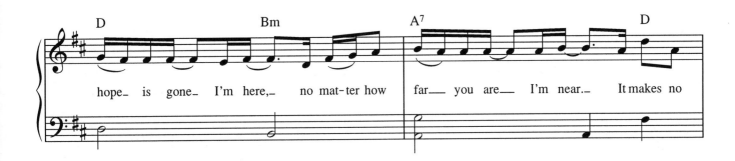

hope__ is gone__ I'm here,__ no mat-ter how far__ you are__ I'm near.__ It makes no

1.

dif - fer -ence who you are,___ I am your an - gel.___ I'll be__ your__

2.

dif-fer-ence who you are,__ I am your an- gel._____

ff

Verse 2:

I saw your teardrops and I hear you crying
All you need is time, seek me and you shall find
You have everything you're still lonely
It don't have to be this way
Let me show you a better day
And then you will see the morning will come
And all of your days will be bright as the sun
So all of your fears, just cast them on me
How can I make you see?

I'll be your cloud *etc.*

On A Day Like Today

Words & Music by Bryan Adams & Phil Thornalley

Moderately

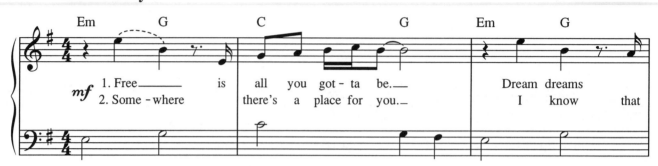

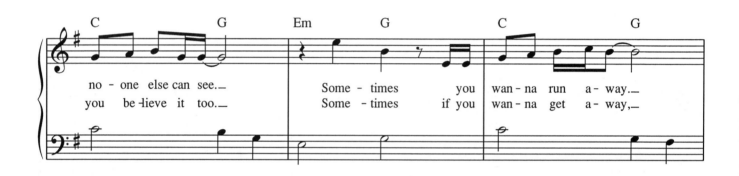

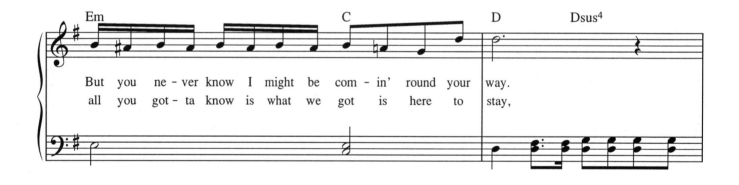

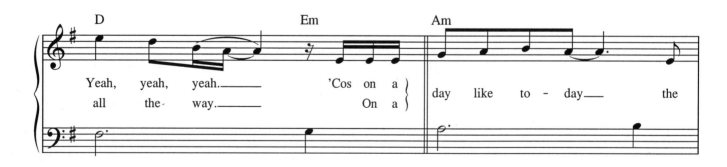

© Copyright 1998 Badams Music Limited (50%) & BMG Music Publishing Limited, Bedford House, 69-79 Fulham High Street, London SW6 (50%).
This arrangement © Copyright 1999 BMG Music Publishing Limited for their share of interest.
All Rights Reserved. International Copyright Secured.

13

no - one com - plains.＿＿ Free to be pure,＿＿＿

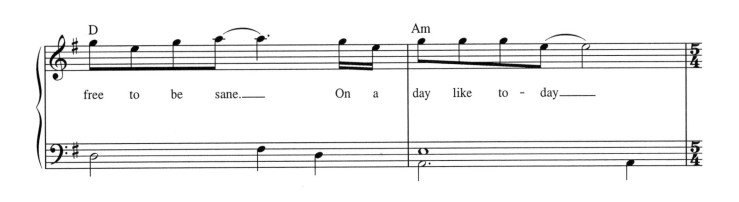

free to be sane.＿＿ On a day like to - day＿＿＿

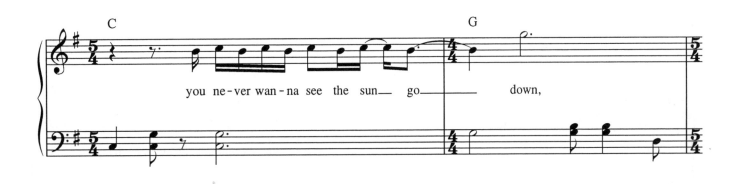

you ne-ver wan-na see the sun＿ go＿＿＿ down,

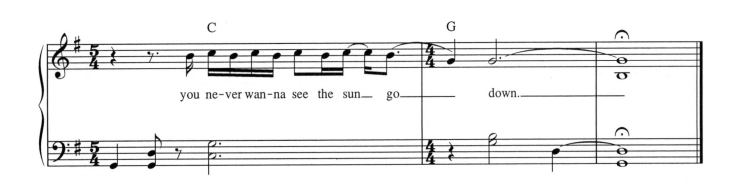

you ne-ver wan-na see the sun＿ go＿＿ down.＿＿

Perfect Moment

Words & Music by James Marr & Wendy Page

Moderately

1. This is my mo-ment, this is my per-fect mo-ment with you.

This is what God meant, this is my per-fect mo-ment with you.

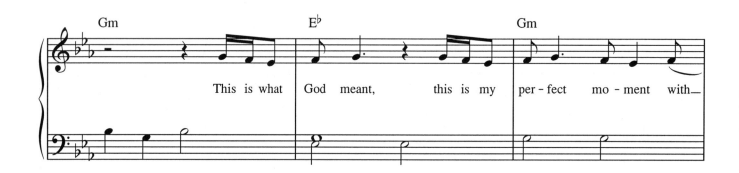

you. Wish I could freeze this space in time, the way that I

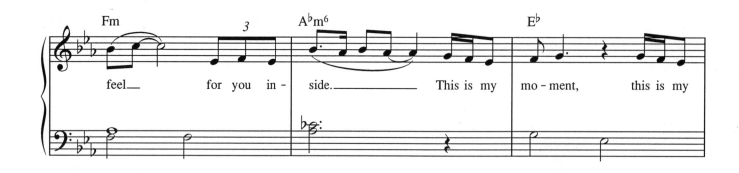

feel for you in-side. This is my mo-ment, this is my

© Copyright 1999 Chrysalis Music Limited, The Chrysalis Building, 13 Bramley Road, London W10 6SP.
All Rights Reserved. International Copyright Secured.

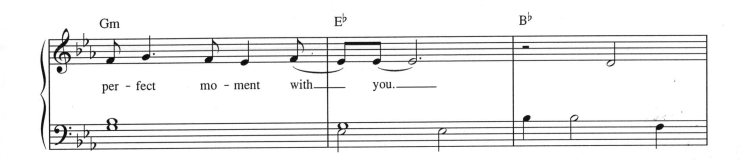

per - fect mo - ment with____ you.____

2. Tell me you love me when you____ leave. You're more than a sha - dow,

that's what I____ be - lieve. You take me to pla - ces I ne - ver thought I'd see.____

Min - ute by min - ute you're the world to me.____ I wish I could frame____ the look in your

eyes,____ the way that I feel for you in - side.____ This is my

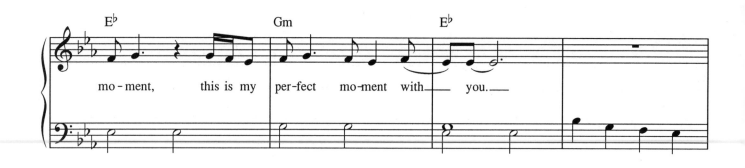

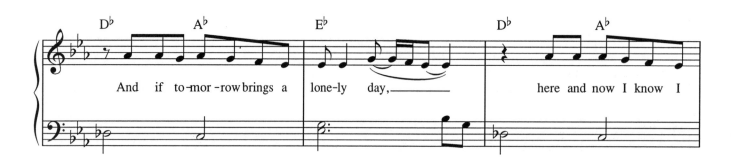

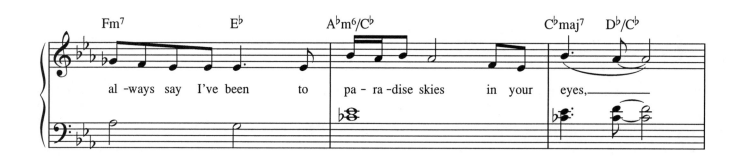

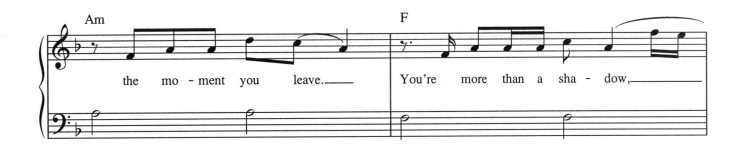

the mo - ment you leave.____ You're more than a sha - dow,____

____ I've got to be - lieve. I wish I could keep you all of my

life,____ the way that I feel____ for you_ in - side.____ This is my

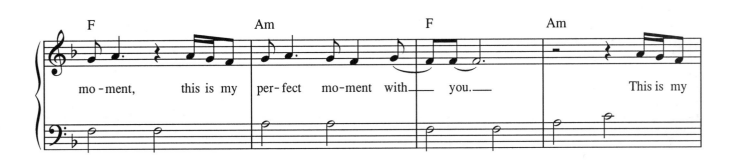

mo - ment, this is my per - fect mo - ment with____ you.____ This is my

mo - ment, this is my per - fect mo - ment with you.____

Look At Me

Words & Music by Geri Halliwell, Andy Watkins & Paul Wilson

Moderately

© Copyright 1999 19 Music Limited/BMG Music Publishing Limited, Bedford House,
69-79 Fulham High Street, London SW6 (66.66%) & Windswept Pacific Music Limited, Hope House, 40 St. Peter's Road, London W6 (33.34%).
This arrangement © Copyright 1999 BMG Music Publishing Limited for their share of interest.
All Rights Reserved. International Copyright Secured.

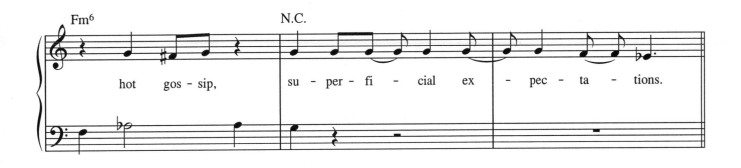

hot gos - sip, su - per - fi - cial ex - pec - ta - tions.

Look at me,___ you can take it it all___

___ be - cause___ this face is free.___

may - be next___ time use___ your eyes___ and look at me.___

I'm a dra - ma queen___ if that's___ your

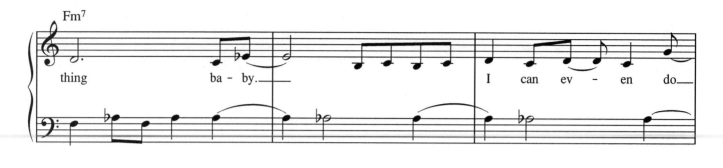

thing ba - by. I can ev - en do

1.

To Coda ⊕ N.C.

re - al - i - ty. Uh! Uh! Uh! Uh!

2. N.C.

Am

That's me!

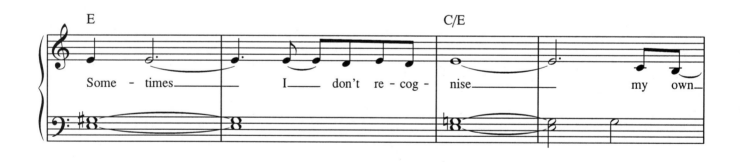

E

C/E

Some - times I don't re - cog - nise my own

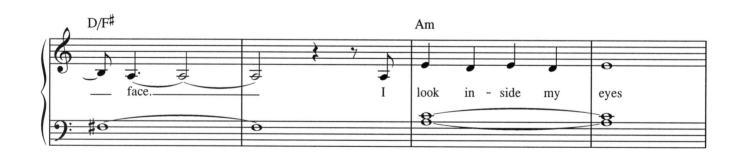

D/F♯

Am

face. I look in - side my eyes

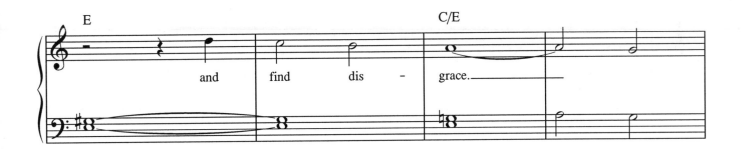

and find dis - grace.

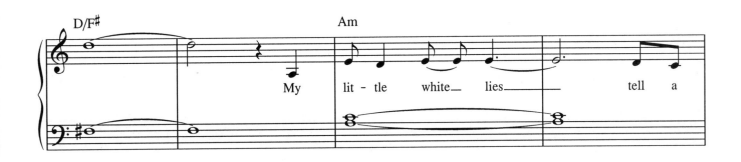

My lit - tle white lies tell a

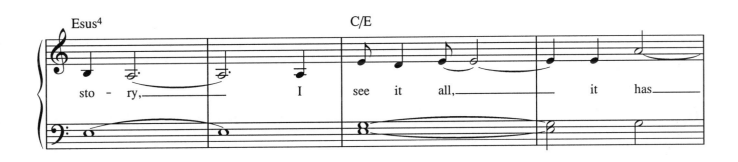

sto - ry, I see it all, it has

no glo - ry. Huh!

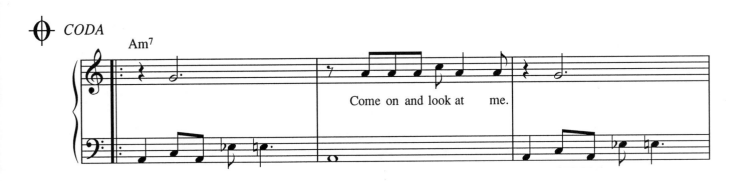

Come on and look at me.

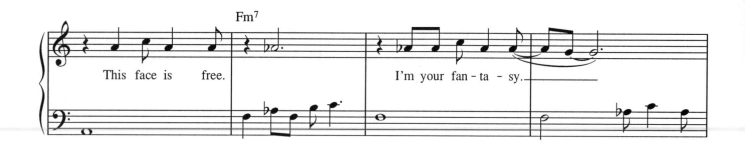

This face is free. I'm your fan - ta - sy.

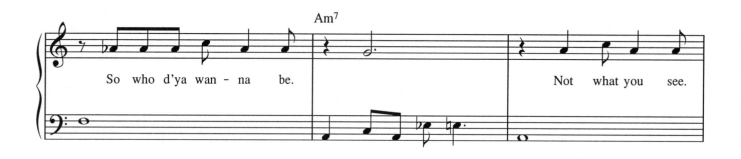

So who d'ya wan - na be. Not what you see.

I'm a dra - ma queen,

Repeat ad lib to fade

if that's your scene. come on and look at me.

Verse 2:

Fake money, real plastic
Stupid cupid, fantastic
Queer thinking, straight talking
What you see ain't what you're getting.
Fast loving, slow moving
No rhythm, but I'm grooving
Old feeling, new beginning
Superficial expectations.

Look at me *etc*.

She

Words by Herbert Kretzmer
Music by Charles Aznavour

Moderately slow

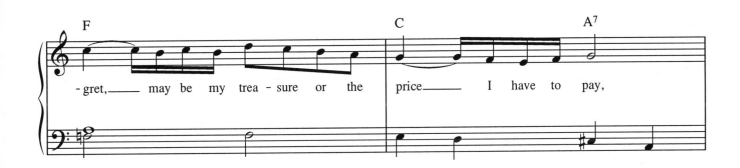

© Copyright 1974 Standard Music Limited, 11 Uxbridge Street, London W8.
All Rights Reserved. International Copyright Secured.

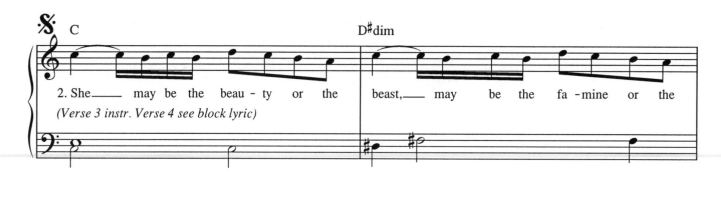

2. She___ may be the beau - ty or the beast,___ may be the fa - mine or the

(Verse 3 instr. Verse 4 see block lyric)

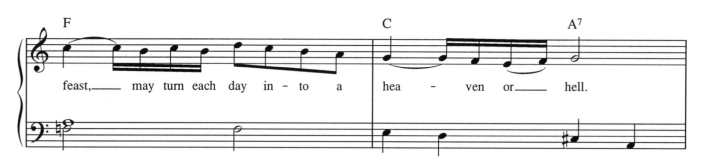

feast,___ may turn each day in - to a hea - ven or___ hell.

She___ may be the mir - ror of my dreams___ a smile re - flec - ted in a

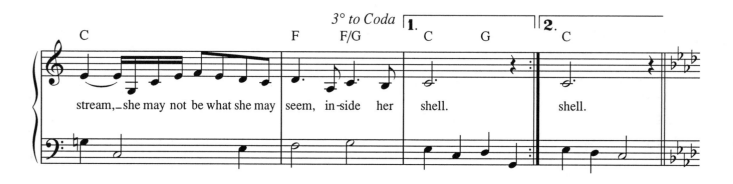

3° to Coda

1. **2.**

stream,___she may not be what she may seem, in -side her shell. shell.

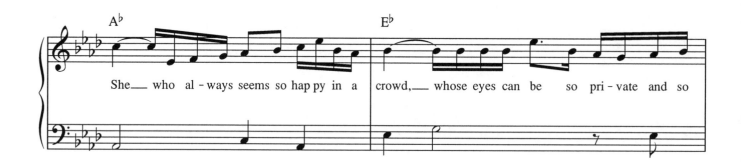

She___ who al - ways seems so hap py in a crowd,___ whose eyes can be so pri - vate and so

proud,_____ no-one's al-lowed to see them when they cry.

She__ may be the love that can-not hope to last,__ may come to me from sha-dows of the

past_____ that I'll re-mem-ber till the day I die.

D.S. al Coda

✛ *CODA*

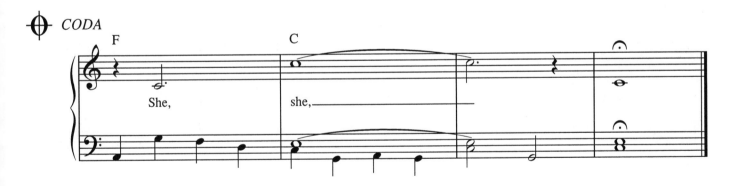

She, she,_____

Verse 4:

She may be the reason I survive
The why and wherefore I'm alive
The one I'll care for through the rough and ready years.
Me, I'll take her laughter and her tears
And make them all my souvenirs
For where she goes I've got to be
The meaning of my life is she, she, she.

Sometimes

Words & Music by Jörgen Elofsson

Moderately slow

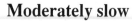

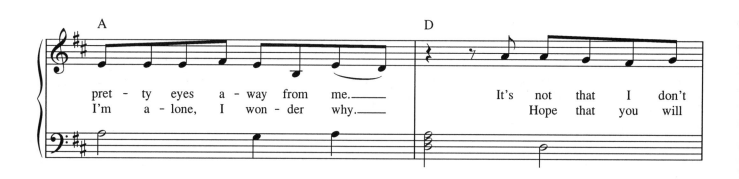

© Copyright 1999 BMG Music Publishing Limited, Bedford House, 69-79 Fulham High Street, London SW6 (25%),
Grantsville Publishing Limited/Zomba Music Publishers Limited, 165-167 High Road, London NW10 (25%) & NCB (50%).
All Rights Reserved. International Copyright Secured.

you right, be with you day and night. Ba-by, all I need is time.

Just hang a-round and you'll see there's no-where I'd rath-er be. If you love me, trust

in me the way that I trust in

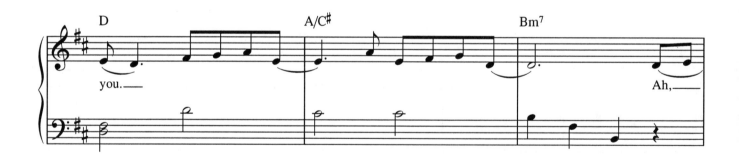

you. Ah,

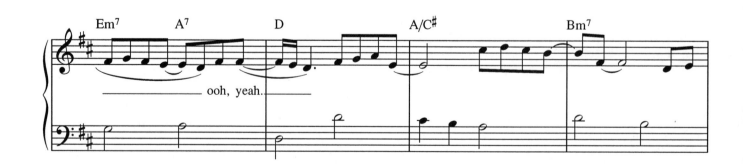

ooh, yeah.

What Can I Do

Words & Music by Andrea Corr, Caroline Corr, Sharon Corr & Jim Corr

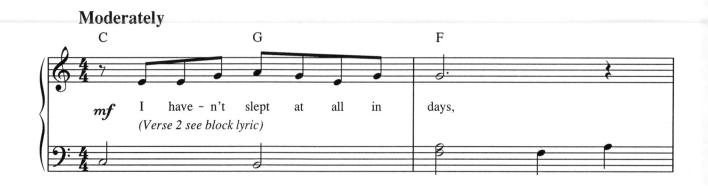

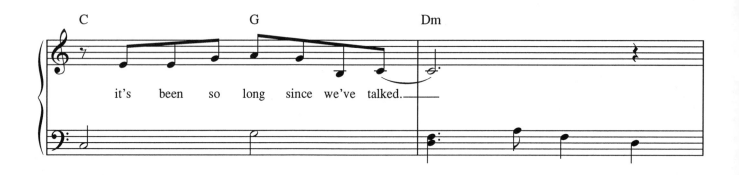

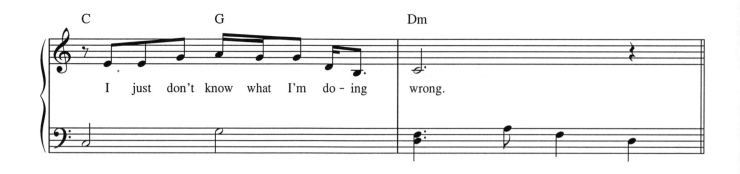

© Copyright 1997 Beacon Communications Music Corporation/Songs of PolyGram International Incorporated, USA.
PolyGram Music Publishing Limited, 47 British Grove, London W4.
All Rights Reserved. International Copyright Secured.

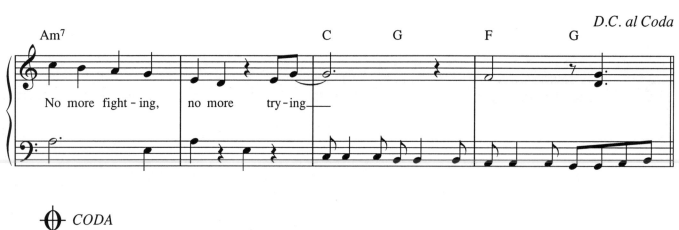

No more fight - ing, no more try - ing

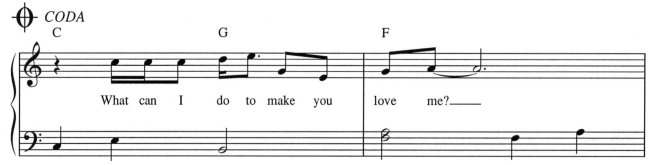

CODA

What can I do to make you love me?

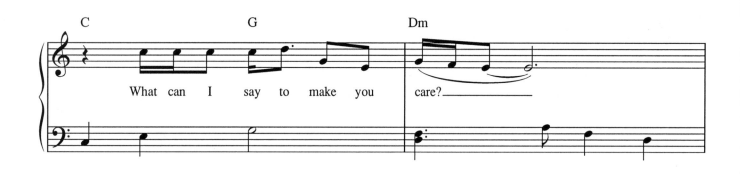

What can I say to make you care?

What can I say to make you feel this?

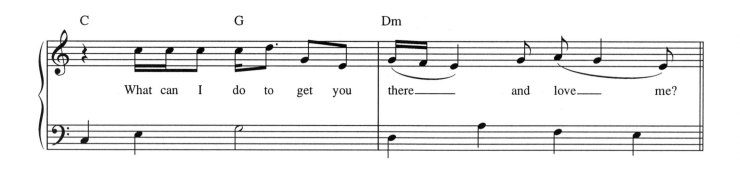

What can I do to get you there and love me?

Verse 2:

There's only so much I can take
And I just got to let it go
And who knows I might feel better
If I don't try and I don't hope.

What can I do...

When The Going Gets Tough

**Words & Music by Wayne Braithwaite, Barry Eastmond,
Robert John 'Mutt' Lange & Billy Ocean**

© Copyright 1985 Zomba Enterprises Incorporated, Aqua Music Limited & Out Of Pocket Productions Limited, USA.
All rights controlled by Zomba Music Publishers Limited, 165-167 High Road, London NW10.
All Rights Reserved. International Copyright Secured.

get my - self 'cross the ri - ver, that's the price___ I'm will - ing to pay.___

(Verse 3 see block lyric)

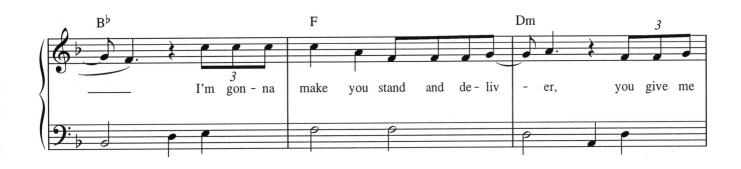

___ I'm gon - na make you stand and de - liv - er, you give me

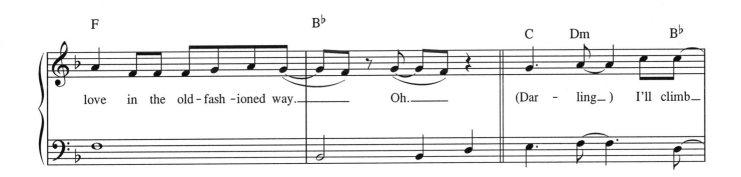

love in the old - fash - ioned way.___ Oh.___ (Dar - ling_) I'll climb

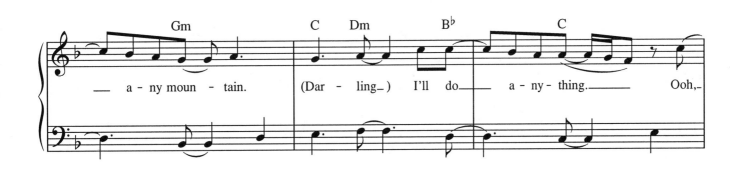

___ a - ny moun - tain. (Dar - ling_) I'll do___ a - ny - thing.___ Ooh,_

_ (ooh,_) can I touch_ you (can I touch you) And do the things that lov - ers do?_

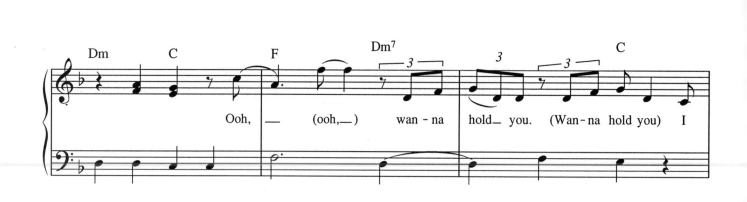

Ooh, _ (ooh,_) wan - na hold_ you. (Wan-na hold you) I

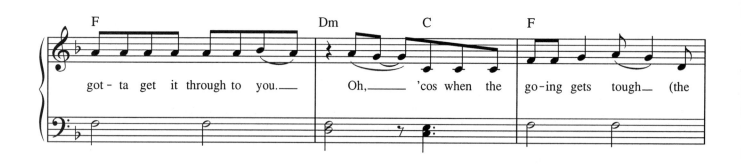

got - ta get it through to you._ Oh,_ 'cos when the go-ing gets tough_ (the

tough get go - ing) When the go - ing gets rough_ oh,_ (the tough get rough) Hey_

(hey)_ hey,_ hey,_ hey,_

1. 3. I'm gon - na

2. Dm | C | Dm | B♭

Dar - ling___ { I'll climb___ a - ny moun - tain } / { I'll reach___ for the hea - ven }

C Dm | **1.** B♭ Gm | **2.** B♭ Gm

Dar - ling___ { I'll swim___ a - ny sea.___ } / { with you___ } ___ lov - ing me.___

N.C. | | F

Ooh,___ | Ooh.___

Verse 3:

I'm gonna buy me a one way ticket
Nothing's gonna hold me back
Your love's like a soul train coming
And I feel it coming down the track.

(Darling) I'll climb any mountain *etc*

You Gotta Be

Lyrics & Melody by Des'ree
Music by Ashley Ingram

Moderately

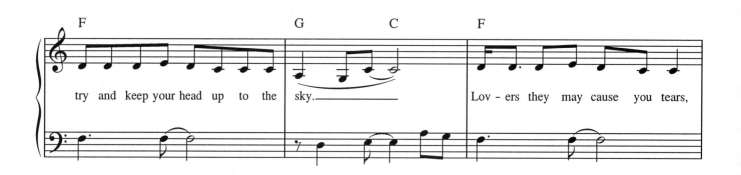

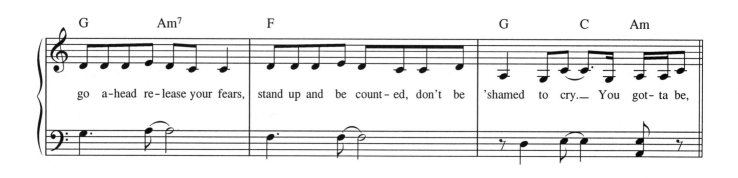

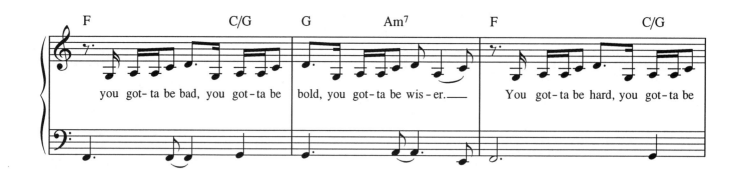

© Copyright 1994 Sony/ATV Music Publishing (UK) Limited, 10 Great Marlborough Street, London W1 (60%)/
BMG Music Publishing Limited, Bedford House, 69-79 Fulham High Street, London SW6 (40%).
This arrangement © Copyright 1999 Sony/ATV Music Publishing (UK) Limited (60%)/BMG Music Publishing Limited (40%).
All Rights Reserved. International Copyright Secured.

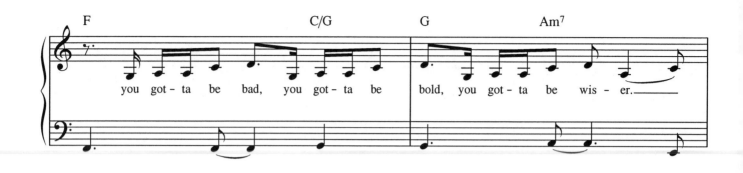

you got-ta be bad, you got-ta be bold, you got-ta be wis-er.

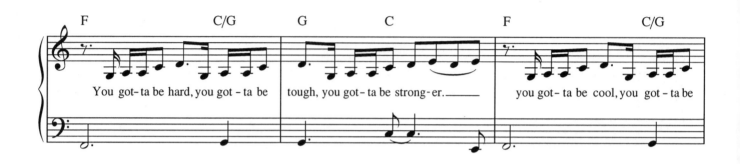

You got-ta be hard, you got-ta be tough, you got-ta be strong-er. you got-ta be cool, you got-ta be

calm, you got-ta stay to-geth-er. All I know, all I know love will save the day.

Time asks no ques-tions, it goes on with-out you, leav-ing you be-hind if you can't

stand the pace, The world keeps on spin-ning, can't stop it if you tried to. The

Verse 3:

Remember listen as your day unfolds
Challenge what the future holds
Try to keep your head up to the sky
Lovers they may cause you tears
Go ahead release your fears.
My, oh my, hey hey.

That Don't Impress Me Much

Words & Music by Shania Twain & Robert John "Mutt" Lange

Moderately

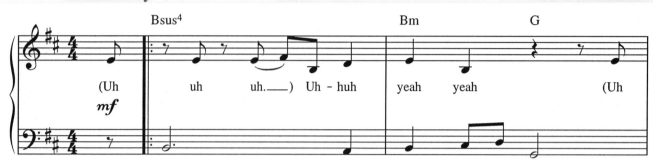

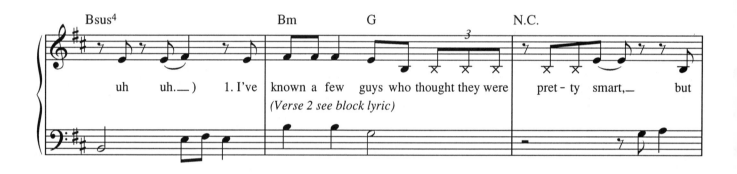

© Copyright 1997 Out Of Pocket Productions & Loon Echo Incorporated/Songs Of PolyGram International Incorporated, USA.
Zomba Music Publishers Limited, 165-167 High Road, London NW10 (50%)/
PolyGram Music Publishing Limited, 47 British Grove, London W4 (50%).
All Rights Reserved. International Copyright Secured.

44

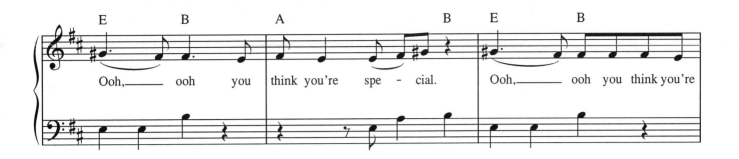

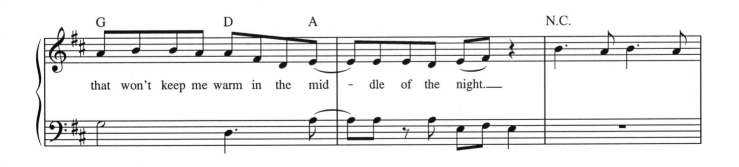

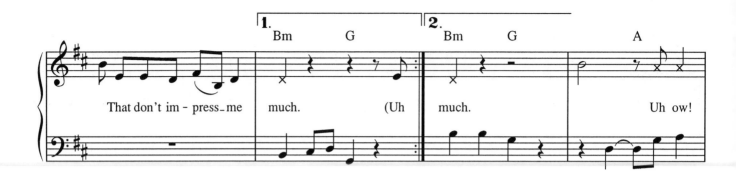

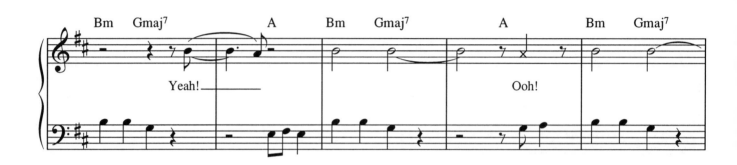

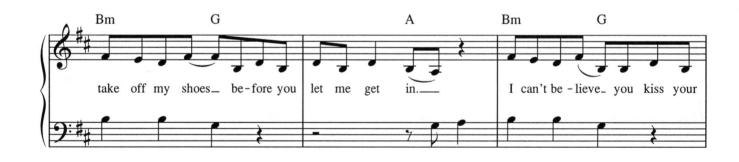

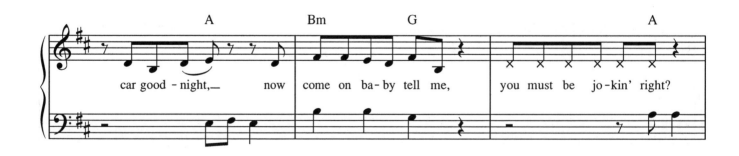

46

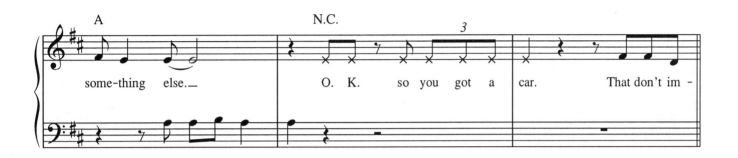

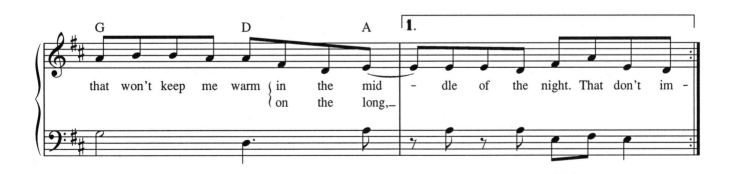

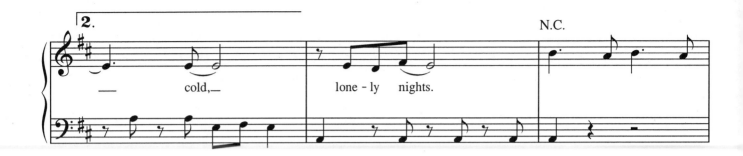

cold,— lone - ly nights.

That don't im - press— me much. (Uh uh uh) Uh huh

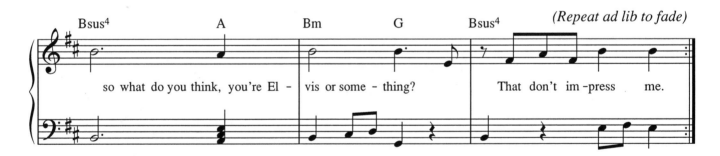

yeah, yeah. (Uh uh uh) *(Spoken)*

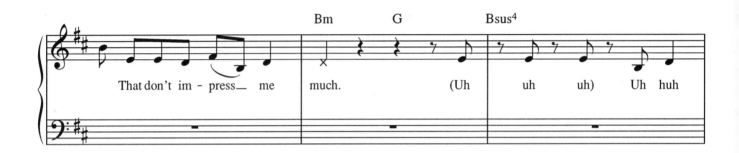

so what do you think, you're El - vis or some - thing? That don't im -press me.

Verse 2:

I never knew a guy who carried a mirror in his pocket
And a comb up his sleeve; just in case
And all that extra-hold gel in your hair oughta lock it
'Cause Heaven forbid it should fall outta place.

Ooh, ooh you think you're special
Ooh, ooh you think you're something else
Okay, so you're Brad Pitt.

That don't impress me much *etc.*